THE STORY OF Scotland's FLAG

AND THE LION AND THISTLE

Text by David Ross
Illustrated by Mike Lacey, Simon Girling and Associates

Reprinted 1999, 2001

Published by Waverley Books Ltd,
David Dale House, New Lanark, ML11 9DJ, Scotland

ISBN 1 902407 05 9

Printed and bound in China

PART ONE

THE SCOTTISH FLAG

Every country has a flag. A flag is just a rectangle of coloured cloth that can be held up or fixed to a pole. But these pieces of cloth, and their colours, are very important to us. The pattern and the colours are special to each country. The flag is shared by everyone in the country: it is a sign of belonging. It shows that we are not simply a group of people living in a particular part of the world, but a nation. We have a shared past and look forward to a shared future, living together in the same land. The flag is the sign of the nation. To Americans, the flag is a reminder of their struggle for freedom in the War of American Independence against Britain. To the French, their red, white and blue flag is a reminder of their revolution, when they fought for the rights of ordinary people. In many countries, to insult or misuse the flag is a crime. And to burn the flag of another country is still seen as a terrible thing to do.

Some flags are very new. Russia changed her flag only a few years ago. But then, some countries are very new. Even countries like Belgium and Italy, partners in the European Union, are less than two hundred years old. Some flags are very old. The Scottish flag is one of these. Its story goes back a long way.

The flag of Scotland is a silver cross on a blue

background. The cross goes from corner to corner: this kind of cross is called a saltire. The flag of England is an upright cross, red on a white background. This is the cross of Saint George, patron saint of England. The saltire is known as Saint Andrew's Cross. Saint Andrew was one of the twelve disciples of Jesus Christ. Like Jesus, he was crucified. The Romans thought he was a dangerous man, spreading wrong ideas among the people, so they had him killed. Andrew asked to be crucified on a cross different from that of his leader, Jesus. He did not think he was good enough for the cross of Christ.

At the time Saint Andrew was killed, Scotland was a faraway country, hardly known at all to the outside world. The few travellers who had been there from Rome thought of it as a cold and misty land, lived in by wild people. They called it Caledonia. Although Roman armies came into Caledonia, its people were never defeated by the Romans.

How then did Saint Andrew become Scotland's saint?

The story is this. After Andrew's death, his body was taken away by his fellow Christians and buried. Because he had been an Apostle (one of the twelve disciples of Jesus Christ), his fame was very great, and people wanted to visit the place where he was buried. They believed that Andrew was in heaven and that he might help in having their prayers answered by God.

Andrew's grave was in Greece, in a place called Patrae. Then, nearly four hundred years after his death, the Emperor Constantius decided that a little place like Patrae was not suitable for keeping the remains of such a great saint as Andrew. He ordered that the bones of the saint be brought to his capital, Constantinople, the greatest city in the world at that time.

The keeper of the saint's remains was a man called Regulus. Now Regulus had a strange dream in which he was visited by an angel. The angel told him that the bones of Saint Andrew should be taken, not to Constantinople, but to a faraway country at the edge of the world. Regulus should take them there and build a church. Regulus obeyed the angel rather than the Emperor. He travelled across Europe, with the remains of Saint Andrew kept in a chest. It was a long, difficult journey. At last he came to the east coast of Caledonia. There, at a place called Muckros, he and his companions landed and set up his church. Beneath the altar, it is said, he buried the chest containing the bones of the Apostle. As the years went by, the name of the place was changed. Regulus himself had been named as a saint, and Muckros became known as Kilrymont – the hill of the church of Regulus. Later still, the fame of

the greater saint overtook that of Regulus, and the place became known as Saint Andrews. Where his little church, made of wood, mud and turf, had been, a splendid stone cathedral was built. You can still see the ancient tower called Saint Rule's Tower (Rule is English for Regulus) beside the now ruined cathedral in Saint Andrews.

It was a proud and very unusual boast for a small country on the edge of Europe to claim that it was the last resting place of one of the Twelve Apostles. Perhaps it was not surprising that people in Scotland should feel that Saint Andrew was very close to them. In fact, at that time Scotland was not a single country but divided into four separate kingdoms. One of these kingdoms was Pictland, and in the year 761, the Picts were fighting the Anglo-Saxons, who lived in the north of England (England was also divided into several kingdoms at that time). The two armies were very near each other when King Angus of the Picts had a dream. He saw Saint Andrew appear to him, bearing his saltire cross. The battle took place on the following day, near the village in East Lothian called Athelstaneford, and the Picts won a great victory. From then on, the saltire was taken as the badge of the Picts, and they adopted

Andrew as their protecting saint. Even when the Pictish kingdom ended and Scotland became a single country, the fame of Saint Andrew was such that he became the patron saint of the whole country.

That is the story. Of course it was not written down until much later, and it is not the kind of story that can be proved. But there were other saints who might have become the patron saint of Scotland, like Saint Columba, who set up the famous abbey on the island of Iona and taught Christianity to the Picts. The story of Saint Regulus and Saint Andrew must have seemed very real to the Scottish people for them to choose Andrew rather than Columba as their protector.

The Beginnings of the Flag

Although the saltire was Scotland's special sign, there was still no flag. Flags had not yet been invented, but there was a need for something like a flag. Often there was fighting between Scotland and England. Men needed to be able to tell who was a friend and who was an enemy. If they were separated from their group, they needed to see where the others were. Each king or captain had his own badge, and his followers looked out for it and often wore it themselves. The same badge, embroidered on a pennant or banner, might be attached to a long spear and held up above the heads of the soldiers. Or it might be set in the ground in

order to provide a rallying point for soldiers who might otherwise spread out and lose themselves in a battle. From this eventually came the flagpole.

One of those many battles happened in 1138 and was called the Battle of the Standard (another word for flag). Some people think that the Scottish king, David the First, used a lion as his personal sign for the first time here. Later in the same century, the Scottish king was called William, and after his death he was called William the Lion. You will find out more about the Scottish lion later in this book. But we do not know what sign was on William's standard.

A more peaceful reason for needing a flag was that the kings of different countries sometimes met in friendship. Then, too, it was necessary to show who were the followers of which king. Each king or captain had his own personal badge, and his followers looked out for that and sometimes wore it. Also, ships were sailing from country to country, and it was useful to show a sign of which country the ship came from.

When King Robert the First defeated the English army at Bannockburn in 1314, there was still no saltire flag, but undoubtedly many Saint Andrew's Crosses were embroidered on the tunics of his men, not only to proclaim their loyalty but also in the hope that the saint would ensure their safety in the fight. In the fourteenth century, Scottish soldiers had a white saltire on the front and back of their tunics. There is a very old flag in the National Museum of Scotland, called the Douglas Standard. It was said to have been used at the Battle of Otterburn in 1388. It was the personal flag of the Scottish Earl of Douglas, and it was green, with a saltire as well as a red heart (the special symbol of the Douglases). This is the oldest flag we have that shows the saltire cross. Otterburn was a famous battle between the Douglases and the English Percy family, from Northumberland. It was won by the Scots, though Douglas himself died in the fight.

It was probably sailors, with their skill in sewing and working with canvas, who first made the kind of flag that can be hoisted on a rope and pulled down again. By this time, the cross of Saint Andrew was already used in many different ways to represent the kingdom of Scotland. It was used on coins (King David the First in the thirteenth century introduced the first Scottish coins). The saltire was already the symbol of the Scottish nation, and when national flags became used, during the fifteenth century, the saltire was the obvious and natural thing to show on it.

The colours, silver on blue, take us back to the story of King Angus's dream, when he saw Saint Andrew bearing a silver cross against the blue of the sky.

The Scots took great pride in their flag. Other countries, like Denmark and Sweden as well as England, had crosses on their flags, but the Scots knew that theirs was not only one of the oldest but also the most powerful. They believed that their flag put them under the special care of Saint Andrew. And it was theirs, the flag of the Scottish people. It flew from the masts of their ships, like Sir Andrew Barton's *The Lion*. Flying above the castles of Edinburgh and Stirling, the flag told the visitor, "You are in Scotland".

When the young Mary Queen of Scots returned from France to rule as queen of Scotland in 1561, it was the saltire flag that greeted her on a misty morning at Leith harbour. At that time, the Scots were changing in the way they thought about God and the church. They set up their own church, which disapproved of prayers to saints, and they broke up the holy pictures and statues in churches. The great cathedral built in honour of Saint Andrew was attacked and ruined. But the saltire cross still flew. Even though it was the sign of a saint, it had also become the sign of the nation, and no one tried to stop it being used.

In 1603, the King James the Sixth of Scotland also became the King James the First of England and went to live in London. Although Scotland and England remained separate, he was keen to turn them into a

single country, and he asked for a flag to be designed that combined the crosses of Saint Andrew and Saint George. The Scots were not at all pleased about this. They did not want to lose their own flag, and the fact that the red cross of Saint George was laid on top of the silver cross of Saint Andrew made them angry. The Scottish parliament complained to the king, and the Saint Andrew's Cross continued to fly in Scotland.

In the seventeenth century, the Scots joined with the English parliament to fight against King Charles the First. They were called the Covenanters, and they did not believe in saints. They would have been shocked at the thought that they needed the protection of a saint, but they carried the flag of Saint Andrew far into England. It stood above their camps and it led them into battle. To many people it became known as the Covenanters' flag. About a hundred years later, when the flag of the United States was designed, its blue background was taken from the Scottish flag – "taken from the Covenanters' banner in Scotland" wrote an American writer.

In the year 1707, Scotland and England finally joined together to become the United Kingdom. A new Union flag was designed, the first form of the "Union Flag" which is still the British flag. This flag has three crosses – the blue and white saltire of Saint Andrew, the red and white cross of Saint George, and the red and white saltire of Saint Patrick. It was ordered that the Union flag "be used in all flags, banners, standards and ensigns both at sea and land". Official buildings, like Edinburgh Castle, now hoisted the Union flag in place of the Scottish saltire.

But the saltire was not forgotten. There were people in Scotland who did not want to be united with England. There were others who did not like the fact that the London parliament had brought in the German Prince George of Hanover to be the king. They wanted the king to come from the Stuart family, who had been kings of Scotland and of England until King James the Second had been forced to give up the throne in 1688. They still saw Saint Andrew's Cross as the true flag of Scotland.

The supporters of the Stuarts were called the Jacobites (meaning "the people of James"), and they carried the saltire of Scotland but with a cross of gold, not white, as blue and gold were the Stuart colours. In this way, at battles like Culloden, the last battle fought on British soil (1746), the cross of Saint Andrew was carried by both sides. Scots fought alongside English and German troops for King George against other Scots who fought with Bonnie Prince Charlie for the Stuarts.

Scotland's cross can also be found in the flags of two Canadian provinces, both of which have many people of Scottish descent – Nova Scotia (the name means New Scotland) and Newfoundland. In their case, the

colours are reversed, with a blue cross on a white background.

Today the Scottish flag is on show more than ever before. It can be seen in hundreds of places throughout the country, from ancient buildings like Blair Castle to modern schools and offices, and soon it will fly above the building of the new Scottish parliament. But nowhere does it fly more proudly than in the village of Athelstaneford, where it is still hoisted daily to remind us of King Angus and his dream, and his battle, all those centuries ago.

PART TWO

The Lion of Scotland and The Thistle

The Lion Rampant

There is another Scottish flag that we often see. This one has a gold background and on it is a red lion standing up on his hind legs, brandishing his claws and with his mouth open to roar. Around the edge is a decorative red double border. The proper name of this flag is the royal standard of Scotland.

Once upon a time, anyone who used this flag without permission would have been severely punished, perhaps even put to death. It was the flag of the king or queen of Scotland. Only he or she was allowed to use it, and it was hoisted only when the king or queen was there in person. It did not belong to the monarch personally. It was used by whoever was king or queen as the sign for all to see that here was the monarch, not any particular man or woman. The king or queen would have his or her own family badge as well, which was personal.

The lion is called the lion rampant. We do not know exactly when it was first used to identify the king. It is likely that early Scottish kings used a dragon as their symbol. The lion may have have begun with William the Lion in the twelfth century, and it was certainly used by his son, King Alexander the Second. We also know that it was used on the Great Seal of Scotland.

This was the stamp placed on all official documents to show that they were not forgeries. Why a lion? Then, as now, the lion was known as the king of the beasts, a fierce and noble animal, dangerous to meddle with. It seemed a very suitable symbol for a king. And partly because their country was a small one, and a rather poor one, compared to England or France, the Scottish kings wanted to make a brave show. It did not not always work out that way. It was under the banner of the lion that King James the Fourth, one of Scotland's most able kings, died fighting the English at the disastrous Battle of Flodden in 1513.

In all the countries of Europe there was a system to record the special badges and symbols of everyone who had such things. These were the lords and their families, as most of the rest of the population had none. This system was called heraldry. The heralds had several jobs to do. They carried the king's messages. They proclaimed the king's greatness. They also kept a record of each family badge. They worked out a way of exactly describing each badge so that it could be drawn and painted by someone who had never seen it. Scotland had its heralds from an early stage and still does. The chief herald is called Lyon King of Arms (the lion again), and he still has powers of his own to prevent people misusing the badges (or coats of arms) that belong to others, and to approve applications for new designs.

Scotland's heralds devised a fine motto to go with the rampant lion. In Latin it reads *Nemo me impune lacessit,* which means in English "No one attacks me and gets away with it". You can see it in many places, including the edges of some one-pound coins.

When King James the Sixth of Scotland also became James the First of England in 1603, a new royal standard was designed that included the symbols of England, France and Ireland as well as the lion

rampant. But the lion standard was still used by the king's chief officer in Scotland. As time went by, it was used less and less. But it was too bright and bold to be forgotten, and from the nineteenth century on, it was manufactured in large quantities as a "Scotch standard", with the suggestion that anyone could use it when they wanted to. Today it is used so widely that we have almost forgotten that it began as a banner that could be used only by the king. Some people even think it is the flag of Scotland.

In the special language of heraldry, Scotland's national badge is "the thistle, slipped and leaved proper". This means that the thistle is face-on, with spines and leaves.

Why a thistle? It is said that early in the eleventh century a raiding party of Danes attacked a Scottish castle. They came by night and took off their shoes to be as quiet as possible. Reaching the castle moat, they jumped in to swim across. To their surprise, the moat held not water but thistles. Their shouts of pain awoke the defenders of the castle, who rushed out, and the Danes fled. Despite this ancient tale, the thistle is not as old a sign as the saltire and the lion. The first time a thistle was used as a special emblem of Scotland was in the time of King James the Third, in the fifteenth century. The saltire had already been in use for more than five hundred years.

Now, the thistle is not a useful plant. Only donkeys eat it. But it is a tough, prickly plant, which you cannot simply grasp hold of and pull out of the ground like a common weed. It was this prickliness that the Scottish heralds liked. In this way it was like the lion with its claws out, and it fitted Scotland's proud motto, *Nemo me impune lacessit*. Perhaps they also had an eye on England. The English flower was the rose (also a

prickly plant). When an English princess, Margaret Tudor, married James's son, it was called the marriage of the thistle and the rose.

The thistle became a popular badge in Scotland. While the lion was grand and the saltire hallowed by long tradition, the homely thistle was something everyone could identify with. To the Scots it was a reminder that their country might not be the most rich or fertile but, equally, it was not to be grasped lightly.

The popular image of the Vikings as ruthless pirates is really only part of their story. A more accurate picture can be drawn by looking at what they themselves left behind.

The photographs and illustrations in this book are based on the many exciting archaeological finds all over the world, from the Viking boots and shoes at York to the great Gokstad ship found nearly one hundred years ago in Norway.

Acknowledgments: Ladybird would like to thank Jeff Watkins and Claire Bylo of the Jorvik Centre, York for their help in making this book and acknowledge the use of additional illustrative material as follows:
Werner Forman Archive (WFA)/Statens Historiska Museum, Stockholm, pages 10, 11, 13 (top), 15, 42 (top), 42 (bottom right), 44 (top); WFA/University, Uppsala, pages 6 (top), 39; WFA/Viking Ship Museum, Bygoløy, title page, 12, 31 (top); WFA/Arhus Museum, Denmark, page 16 (bottom); WFA/Stofnun Arna Magnússonar á Islandi, 36 (top); WFA/National Museum, Copenhagen, 41 (bottom); WFA, pages 13 (bottom), 36 (bottom), 37; Photoresources, pages 5, 6 (bottom), 7, 26 (top); Antikvarisk-topografiska arkivet, Stockholm, page 16 (top), 42 (bottom left); York Archaeological Trust (YAT), pages 17, 19, 21 (top), 46-47 and references for line drawings on page 18 and 38 inc. photograph by Mike Duffy; Mats Wibe Lund, 26 (bottom); John Freeman & Co. (Photographers) Ltd., pages 30, 48/49; University Museum of National Antiquities, Norway, pages 21 (bottom), 32, 33 (top), 38 (top), 41 (top); Grethe Schantz, page 33 (bottom); Trustees of the British Museum, 44 (bottom); Scottish Tourist Board, 50; National Museums of Scotland, 43; Anne Buxton, line drawings on pages 17, 38 and 51.

British Library Cataloguing in Publication Data

Barton, Stephanie
The Vikings.—(A Ladybird book. Series 861, v. 20)
1. Vikings—Juvenile literature
I. Title II. Hook, Richard III. Series
948′.02 DL65

ISBN 0-7214-0945-8

First edition

Published by Ladybird Books Ltd Loughborough Leicestershire UK
Ladybird Books Inc Lewiston Maine 04240 USA

Printed in England

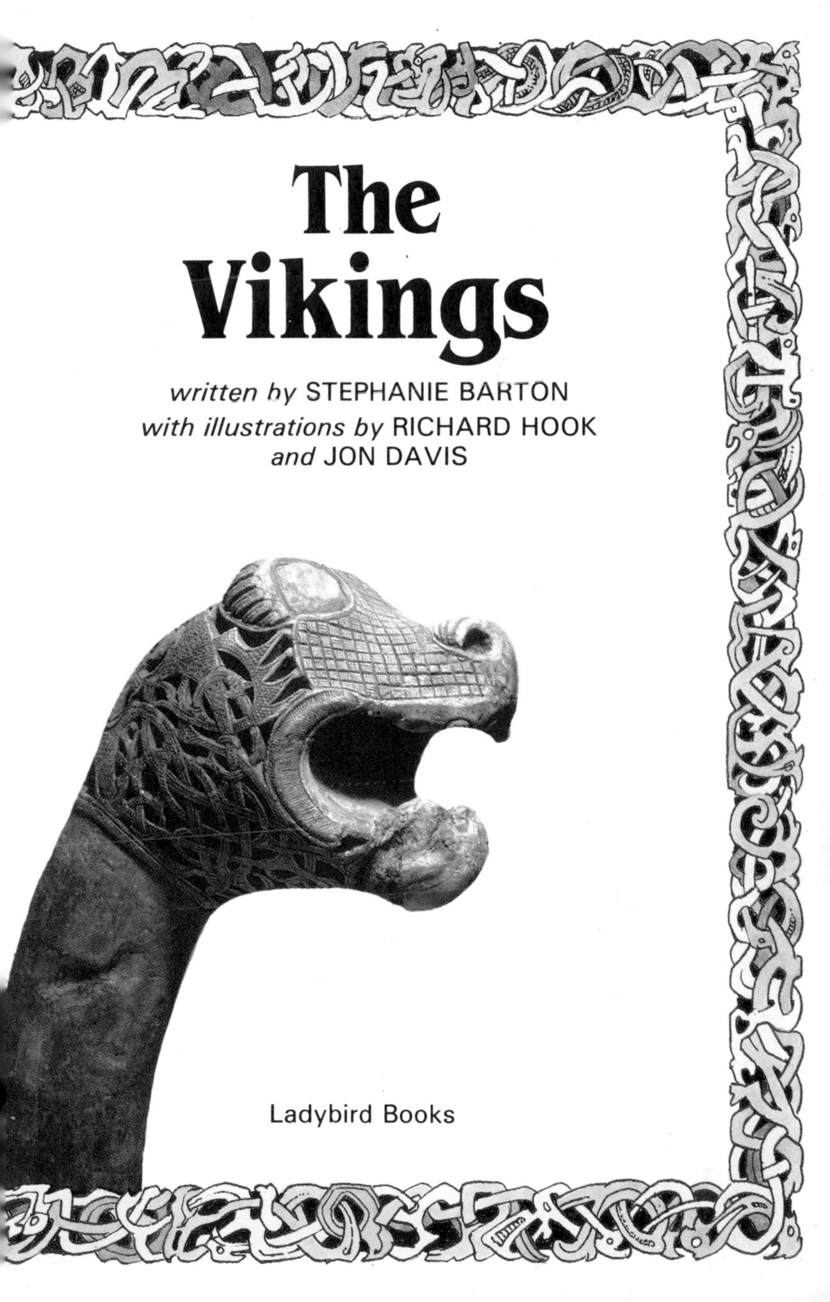

The Vikings

written by STEPHANIE BARTON
with illustrations by RICHARD HOOK
and JON DAVIS

Ladybird Books

Who were the Vikings?

The Vikings lived over a thousand years ago. They came from a vast area of land that is now called Scandinavia – Denmark, Norway and Sweden. Their homelands stretched far north into the Arctic Circle and south to the milder climate of the country of the Danes, a distance of about 1300 miles (2092 km).

The Viking Age lasted 300 years from around AD 800-1100. During that time many Viking ships sailed out from Scandinavia. Not all these sailors were pirates and raiders; there were explorers, merchants and settlers too, who left their homes in search of new lands, wealth and a new life.

Norway

The Anglo-Saxons, living in Britain, called the Scandinavians *Northmen* or *Danes* and to the Franks from France they were *Normans.* Later the Icelandic saga-writers called them the *Vikings*. *Viking* meant piracy or pirate raid and *vikingr* was used to describe a man who was a pirate or raider. No one is sure where the term comes from. Perhaps it came from the Old Norse word *vik* which meant bay, inlet or creek so a Viking was a pirate hidden in a bay or creek.

Of course not all Scandinavians went on pirate raids. Many stayed at home working as farmers, fishermen and craftsmen. Others, like one Norseman called Svein Asleifsson, who lived on the Isle of Orkney in the 12th century, were part-time raiders. Svein's story is told in the *Saga of the Men of Orkney*:

Svein would do much hard work in the spring. But when his work was ended, he would go a-viking and would raid the Scottish Isles and Ireland, and he would come home at midsummer. This he called his 'spring viking'.
(Svein also went a-viking in the autumn once the harvest had been gathered in.)

Viking people

Harald Bluetooth, Eirik Bloodaxe, Svein Forkbeard, Harald the Fair-Haired, Harald the Hard-Ruler and Cnut the Great were some of the Viking kings who ruled in Scandinavia. Stories about their lives were passed from family to family and were told at feasts and courts by the travelling poets or *scalds*.

The Old Norse sagas can still be read today. These tales of adventure, exile, heroes and gods are full of fascinating detail about the Viking way of life. A great Icelandic chieftain and poet, Snorri Sturluson wrote this collection of stories, called the Prose Edda *in the thirteenth century*

A silver cup found in one of the royal burial chambers at Jelling, Denmark

Kings and princes were the most important people in the Viking world. At the beginning of the Viking Age there were many kingdoms in Scandinavia, each ruled by its own king. Sometimes one king would try to establish his own rule over the others, resulting in war between kingdoms. Each kept a household of warriors to fight for him and they were rewarded with gifts of gold, weapons, clothes and land.

A burial mound probably for King Gorm and his wife Thyri has been excavated at Jelling. Their son, King Harald Bluetooth erected this rune-stone for them. The stone is decorated with inscriptions and a wonderful beast fighting a snake. The paint is modern

Jarls were chieftains and aristocrats. They were very powerful and important landowners and the sagas tell us that a jarl was tall, fair-haired and rosy-cheeked. In one Icelandic poem called the *Rigsðula* we are told that a jarl's 'eyes were as keen as a young serpent's' and that he enjoyed sports like fencing, horse riding and swimming.

The freemen or *karls* made up the largest group of men living in Scandinavia. They worked as farmers, fishermen and skilled craftsmen such as boat-builders, house-builders or weapon-makers.

Family life was important. Women ruled the Viking household and often ran the farmstead when their husbands were away. Children were expected to work hard. Young boys were sometimes sent to other households or on a journey or voyage to learn new crafts and skills.

The Vikings captured and traded slaves wherever they went. Many slaves or *thralls* worked on farms or as household servants, doing the dirty and unpleasant jobs. Their owners could buy and sell them as they wished. A thrall's life was a miserable one and it's no wonder that the *Rigsðula* poem tells us that the thrall's back was bent and that he had 'lumpy knuckles and thick fingers' from all the work he had to do!

Gods and religion

At the beginning of the Viking Age the Vikings believed in many gods. They were pagans. The one-eyed *Odin* was the god of war, poetry and wisdom. He was the master of spells and magic. Odin was lord of *Valhalla* (the hall of the slain) and he lived there with his servants, the *Valkyries*, his two ravens and his wolves. The Vikings believed that all warriors who were killed on the battlefield went to Valhalla where they enjoyed everlasting rounds of fighting and feasting.

Odin's eight-legged horse, Sleipnir, said to be carrying either Odin or a dead warrior to Valhalla

Thor was the most popular god. Many men and women took his name as part of their own, such as Thorfinn and Thorjodhil. Thor was the god of the sky and storms and was never without his hammer, *Mjolliner* (meaning lightning). The Vikings looked to Thor to protect them and they made charms and jewellery in the shape of his hammer to bless Viking brides and new-born babies.

During festivals and burial ceremonies the Vikings sometimes made animal and even human sacrifices. An Arab traveller and diplomat, Ibn Fadlan, saw the cremation burial of a Swedish Viking chief in Russia in the year 922. The chief was placed in a tent inside his ship. By his side were his animals, weapons and food and drink for the journey to the Next World. Ibn Fadlan looked on as an old woman, called the Angel of Death, killed a slave girl and laid her beside her master in the ship. Then everything was burned.

This 'horn of plenty' was found in the grave of a Swedish Viking

The graves of ordinary Vikings were often marked with stones arranged in the shape of a ship which they believed would carry the dead person's spirit into the Next World. More important people were buried inside their ships. In the middle of the ninth century two ladies, probably a princess and her slave, were buried in the Oseberg ship. The ship was excavated in Norway over eighty years ago

When the Vikings began to settle in Christian countries, like England and Ireland, more and more of them began to accept the Christian faith. King Olaf Tryggvasson of Norway was converted to Christianity and sent missionaries to colonies like Greenland, where Thjodhild, Eirik the Red's wife, built one of Greenland's first churches.

But some Vikings did not give up their old gods. Many of them worshipped both the Christian God *and* the pagan gods. In the year 1000, Thorgeir, the Lawspeaker at the Icelandic Assembly, declared that all Icelanders should be baptised as Christians. Iceland was now officially a Christian country, but Thorgeir also said that the people could continue to worship their own gods, as long as they did it in secret!

A pre-Viking stamp used for making helmet plaques showing two dancing figures, probably followers of Odin. One wears a horned helmet for the ceremony

In 930 Iceland had its first national assembly – called the ***Althing****. It was held at Thingvellir for two weeks every summer from then on and it was here, in the year 1000, that a law was passed making Iceland a Christian country*

Viking law

The Vikings had one of the earliest forms of law courts, called *Things*. The Thing was a local meeting which might last for several days and was held every year, usually in the summer. Any freeman who had a complaint or quarrel to settle could speak at the gathering and ask for a judgement.

The Vikings respected the law but sometimes there were violent, long-lasting feuds between different families that the Thing could do little to settle. The Viking family was large and if a man was killed his family would take revenge against the murderer's family. Finally the quarrel might be settled by 'blood-money' being paid to the victim's family.

Sometimes a quarrel was settled by *duelling*. A duelling ring was marked out by a cloth laid on the

ground and fixed with pegs. The two men fought until blood was spilled but if one of the men stepped out with one foot he was said to be 'in retreat'; if he stepped out with both feet he was said to be 'running'. The man would be called a coward and this was the worst disgrace of all.

Trial by *ordeal* was another way of ending an argument. Ordeals were usually used when there was not enough evidence against a person and the case was to be judged by the gods. One ordeal used for women was called *ketiltak* (cauldron-taking). The woman had to pluck stones from a vat of boiling water. If the wounds on her hands healed she was said to be innocent!

Thieves were hanged and witches were stoned or drowned but, for a proud Viking, the worst punishment of all was to be made an outlaw. An outlawed man was called *skógarmaðr* (forest-man). He lost all his goods and rights and people were not allowed to feed him or give him shelter. He had to leave the country or live in the forests, alone.

Many Vikings could not read or write and so the rules of law were passed by word of mouth. Those who could write used an alphabet which was made up of sixteen letters or runes. The alphabet was called ***futhark*** *after the first few letters. There were no curves so it was ideal for carving on wood, stone, metal or bone*

What the Vikings looked like

When Ibn Fadlan met a group of Viking merchants in Russia he said that the Viking men were tall and strong with blond hair. They had a ruddy complexion and wore tattoos on their arms. The women wore silver or gold rings round their necks. Each one carried a container at her breast, made of gold, silver, copper or iron, depending on her man's wealth.

Some Viking carvings have survived to show us how the Vikings saw themselves. One is an elk-horn carving, found at Sigtuna in Sweden.

The man on the Sigtuna carving wears a moustache and pointed helmet

When they came to England, the Anglo-Saxon men complained that the Vikings bathed on Saturdays, combed their hair, and changed their clothes too often, making them altogether too popular with the Anglo-Saxon ladies! Another Arab writer who visited the busy Viking market town of Hedeby in Denmark tells us that both the Viking men and women liked to wear make-up on their eyes, to make themselves look more attractive.

Large, bushy eyebrows and a curly moustache: thought to be the face of the Viking god, Loki

What they wore

The Vikings liked to wear fine clothing and jewellery. Viking women would spin, weave and dye their own cloth. In south Scandinavia flax was grown and used to make linen. Fine woollen cloth was sometimes imported from Frisia (now part of the Netherlands) and silks came from Byzantium and China. Animal furs were brought from the Arctic for cloaks and animal skins were used for footwear.

Brightly coloured fabrics were popular and were often woven with patterns. Most of the dyes they used came from plants like *madder* which gave a deep brick-red colour.

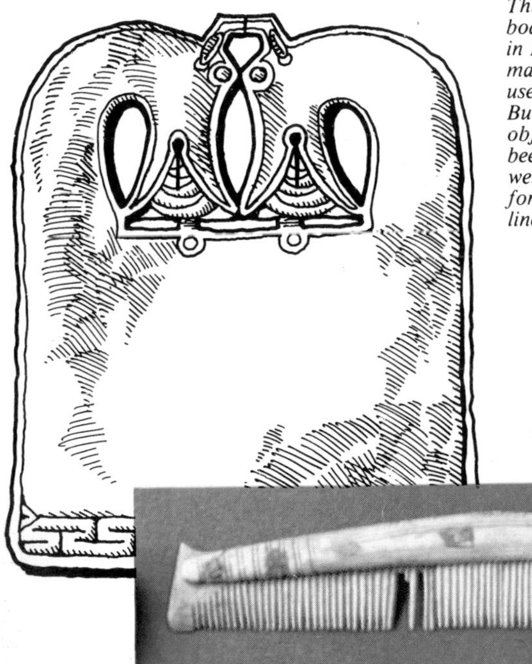

This whalebone board was found in Norway and may have been used for 'ironing'. Bun-shaped glass objects have also been found and were perhaps used for smoothing out linen

An antler comb found in York

When archaeologists investigated the Viking graves at Birka, one of the great Viking trading centres in Sweden, it was in the men's graves and not the women's that traces of rich silk cloth and gold and metal braid were found, more evidence to show that the Viking men took a great pride in their appearance.

A man wore a shirt or *kirtle* which usually had sleeves. The sagas tell us that men also wore short-sleeved undershirts made from linen or wool.

How a leather shoe is made

1 First the upper is cut (from sheep skin or calf skin)...

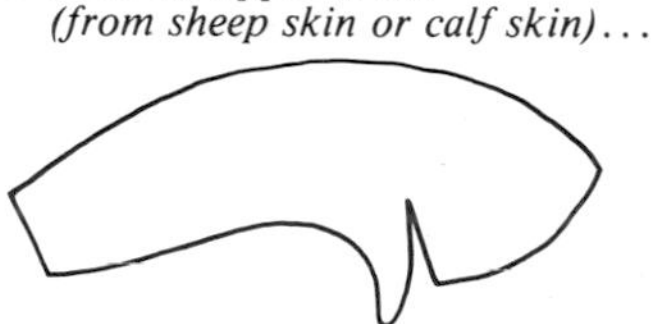

2 ...and then the sole is cut (from cattle hide). The stitching holes are then punched around the edges of both

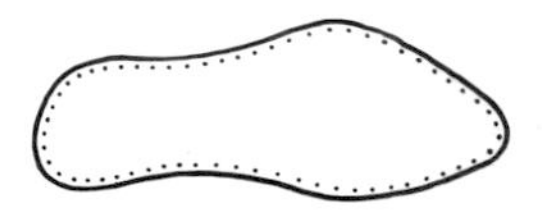

3 Then the shoe is stitched inside out on a wooden foot-shaped block (called a LAST) using linen thread or leather thongs

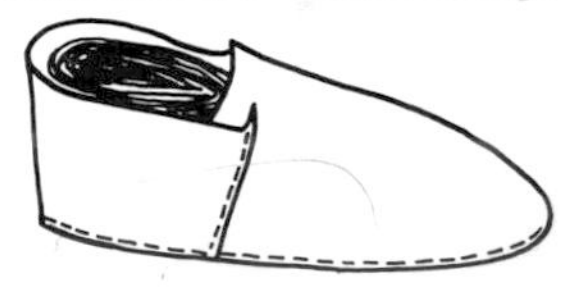

Shaggy fur or cloth cloaks were worn. Their lengths varied. Fragments of the tapestry found on the Oseberg ship show men in short cloaks; others hung to the ground like those the men are wearing in carvings on Viking stones found in Gotland, Norway.

The shape and length of trousers also varied. Merchants and traders picked up new ideas about how to dress from their travels and some wore baggy eastern-style trousers.

The sagas tell us that it was fashionable for a while to wear skin-tight trousers – some were so tight that they were difficult to get on and off! They also tell us that men often wore undertrousers for extra warmth.

Leather footwear found at York

Andersen's replica of the Gokstad ship, seen here in Chicago after its voyage across the Atlantic in 1893

Experiments with replicas

Modern boat builders have made replicas of several Viking ships. The first replica of the Gokstad ship was made by a Norwegian, Magnus Andersen, in 1893. He and his crew sailed the boat across the Atlantic Ocean from Norway to Newfoundland. The ship logged fantastic speeds of over 10 knots and the journey took only twenty eight days.

In 1981, a group of Danes began to build an exact copy of a small Viking trading boat found in the Roskilde Fjord, Denmark. The replica ship, called *Roar Ege*, used 25 tons of oak and fir wood. After 15 000 man-hours the ship was finished and launched into the Roskilde Fjord, where the original had sailed nearly 1000 years before.

Roar Ege

Viking exploration

In Scandinavia the long winters were cold and freezing. The land was so poor that many Viking farmers were unable to grow enough food to feed their large families. As a result, towards the end of the 8th century many left their homelands to go in search of new land.

The Vikings achieved fantastic sea journeys without the use of compasses, although they may have used an instrument called a ***bearing dial*** *to help them to navigate in open seas. They navigated by the moon, stars and the sun. They knew about the clouds, different birds, sea creatures and landmarks that they might see on their voyage – and all this they carried in their heads.*

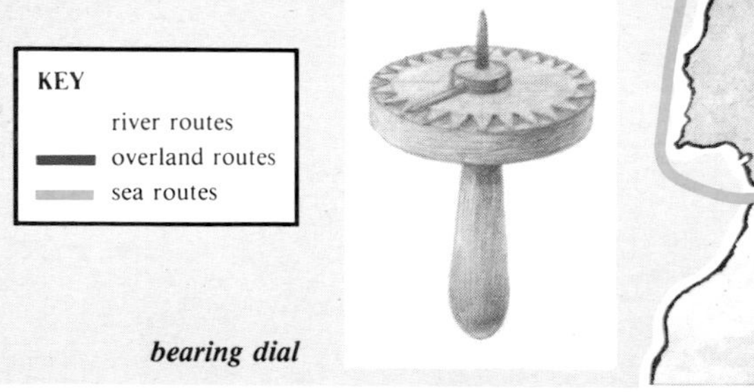

bearing dial

CHINA
NORWAY
SWEDEN
FINLAND
Birka
Kaupang
DENMARK
Hedeby
Volga
Dvina
Elbe
Kiev
Vistula
Dneiper
USSR
Rhine
Paris
Seine
Danube
Loire
BLACK SEA
CASPIAN SEA
TURKEY
Constantinople (Byzantium)
ITALY
Baghdad
Jerusalem
MEDITERRANEAN SEA
NORTH AFRICA

Explorers

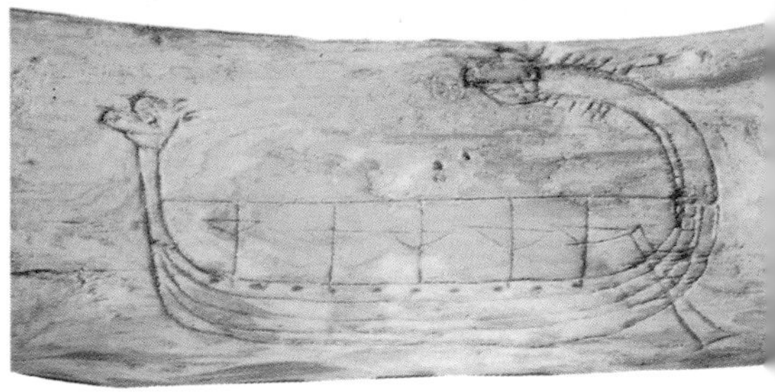

The Vikings of Norway sailed west to the Orkney Islands, the Shetlands and the Outer Hebrides. Some settled in these places, building their houses out of turf and local stone. Others sailed further south to Ireland and the Isle of Man.

In about 860 some Viking explorers, blown off course, sighted an unknown land covered in ice and snow. Ten years later the first Scandinavians came to settle on this volcanic island which they called *Ísland* (Ice Land).

One of the most famous Icelanders was Eirik the Red, so called because of his red hair and fiery temper. His story is told in the Icelandic saga *Eirik the Red* where we learn that he was banished from Norway because of 'some killings'. He came to Iceland and further killings there led him to sail westwards in search of new land. And he found it. In 986 Eirik set up the first Norse colony at Brattahlid (Steep Slope) in a land which he called *Grœnland* (Green Land).

Greenland

◀ *A Norse ship carved in wood*

Later that year another Norwegian, Bjarni Herjolfsson, left Iceland to visit Eirik's settlement in Greenland. Bjarni was lost in fog and blown off course. He sighted an unknown land but sailed on. The land that Bjarni saw was North America. But it was Eirik the Red's son, Leif, who first landed there, some four hundred years before Christopher Columbus.

Many other expeditions set off for Vinland from Brattahlid but the native peoples, whom the Norsemen called *skraelings* (wretches), were hostile and finally the Viking settlers were driven out.

Brattahlid – it was from here that Leif Eiriksson and other members of his family left to settle in a region of America which they called Vinland. Eirik's saga says of Vinland: '...there were wheatfields growing wild there and grown vines. There were also those trees which are called maple...'

The whereabouts of Viking Vinland remains a mystery. Archaeologists have found the ruins of several Viking turf-built buildings at L'Anse aux Meadows in north Newfoundland but as yet there is very little evidence to show where the Vikings went in America.

Merchants and traders

Trading was a way of life for the Vikings and, unlike the pirate raiding ships, Viking merchant ships were made welcome wherever they went. Viking traders also travelled overland with pack horses, carts, skis, skates and sledges into Europe, Britain (including Ireland) and Greenland.

When it was excavated, this richly decorated wagon from the Oseberg ship burial mound was crushed flat and had to be carefully rebuilt. It was probably used to carry the dead princess: the main part of the wagon can be lifted off from the wheels. Similar simpler wagons would have been used for day-to-day work in Viking times

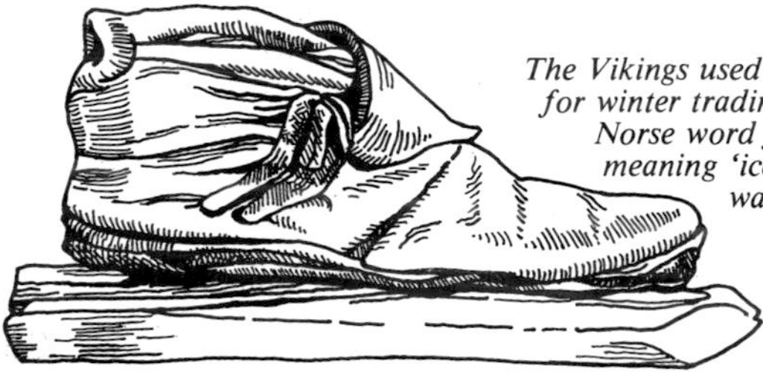

The Vikings used bone skates and skis for winter trading journeys. The Old Norse word for skate is íśleggr *– meaning 'ice legbone'. The bone was smoothed down on one side and cut to fit the foot*

Silver and gold coins from other countries were greatly prized by Viking merchants. Most merchants carried pairs of small portable scales like these. Coins were cut up at the markets and weighed out. The weight would sometimes be added to with 'hack-silver' (silver bracelets or necklaces which were cut up)

Swedish Vikings tackled dangerous river journeys which took them deep into the heart of Russia, onward to the Caspian Sea and then overland by camel to Baghdad. Others followed the River Dneiper through Russia and on to the riches of the Byzantine Empire and its capital, Constantinople, which the Vikings called *Mikligarðr*, the Great City.

The merchants risked their lives and travelled thousands of miles in search of silks, gold, silver, slaves, spices and jewellery which they brought back to trade in the Viking market towns.

These towns became thriving, prosperous work places for craftsmen such as weavers, glass-makers, potters, blacksmiths, leather-workers and carpenters. In one of the houses excavated at Hedeby lumps of raw amber were found, together with some half-finished amber beads. Iron-ore from Sweden was beaten down and made into tools and weapons there and reindeer antlers were made into knife handles, gaming pieces and combs. The Vikings also traded slaves at Hedeby.

Viking warriors and weapons

The ordinary Viking farmer, fisherman, sailor and merchant had to be able to fight. Weapons were important and many took their favourite swords with them to the grave.

Some Vikings hired themselves out as fighters to local chiefs in Scandinavia or in other countries. In Constantinople they served in the Imperial Guard for the Emperor of Byzantium. One of the most famous Vikings to fight for the Emperor was Harald Sigurdson, who later became King of all Norway and was nicknamed Harald the Hard-Ruler.

Only kings and rich chieftains could afford to wear a mail-shirt or armour. Most Vikings wore a padded leather jerkin over their ordinary clothes.

Weapons had to be strong and were beautifully crafted. A Viking sword was often passed down from father to son. The sagas tell us that Viking swords had names like *The Fierce* and *Leg-Biter*.

Viking shields were sturdy and made of wood with an iron boss in the centre. The shields found in the Gokstad ship burial measured a metre across. They had been painted yellow or black and the outside edge had been trimmed in leather.

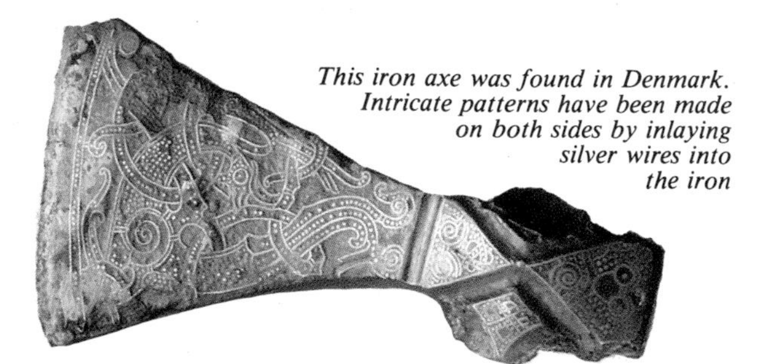

This iron axe was found in Denmark. Intricate patterns have been made on both sides by inlaying silver wires into the iron

This pendant was found in a woman's grave and shows a man, thought to be a priest of Odin, carrying weapons and wearing a horned helmet

Carvings and ornaments show that the Vikings wore simple pointed or rounded helmets, made of iron or leather. The ordinary warrior *never* wore a horned helmet as is often seen in pictures and films!

No actual helmet surviving from the Viking period has horns on it. Horned helmets did exist but they were rare and only used as part of religious festivals.

These Swedish helmets date from the 7th century, about 150 years before the Viking period

Sea and land battles

During sea battles, ships could be roped together making one long floating platform from which the Vikings threw spears, shot bows and arrows and fought in hand-to hand combat with the enemy.

On land, tactics were basic and simple; they fought on foot and formed themselves into a line facing the enemy.

Some warriors made a 'shield-fort' around their chief and the banner.

This 'berserkir' chess-piece comes from the Isle of Lewis, Scotland. The berserkir (which meant 'bear-shirt') were much-prized warriors. Before battle the berserkir dressed in animal skins and worked themselves into a battle frenzy. Snorri Sturluson, one of the saga writers, says that '...they were as mad as dogs or wolves, bit their shields, and were as strong as bears or wild bulls...'

Viking invasion

In the year 793 *'ravages of heathen men miserably destroyed God's church on Lindisfarne, with plunder and slaughter'*. This was how the writers of the *Anglo-Saxon Chronicle*, a record of important events, begun in the late 9th century, described the coming of the Danes. The Viking attacks on England had begun!

A fierce-looking helmet from Sweden, dating from just before the Viking Age

Over the next few years the Vikings came again and again to the English shores in search of treasure and slaves. They came in boatloads in summer, raiding and looting and then returning home before winter set in. In 865 a 'Great Army' of Vikings came to East Anglia where they spent the winter. In the same year, three hundred Viking boats sailed up the Thames and stormed London and Canterbury.

A Viking silver hoard was found at Cuerdale, Lancashire, containing some 4000 silver coins and pieces of hack-silver

The following year the Vikings marched north and captured York. Soon they conquered Northumbria and took land in Mercia. Of the Anglo-Saxon kings only King Alfred held out in his kingdom of Wessex. Eventually Alfred made a treaty with the Vikings. It was agreed that they should be allowed to live in the north and east of England. This area became known as *Danelaw* where Viking law and customs were followed.

In Ireland the Vikings raided and then settled in Dublin. The town became an important and wealthy trading centre. It was protected by a great earth wall and was ideally placed for merchants travelling between Norway and Iceland in the north, and England, France and other countries further south.

York – a Viking capital

When the Vikings captured York in the 860s it was already a busy trading place. York was ruled by Viking kings for nearly eighty years until Eirik Bloodaxe was driven out by the English king, Eadred, in 954.

The Romans founded the city of York but its modern name comes from the Vikings who called it *Jorvik*. Evidence of a town crowded with merchants and craftsmen is being found all the time.

The modern street names give interesting clues to the town's Viking past. Coppergate (Norse *gata* means 'street') was a centre for coopers or wood-carvers; and Skeldergate was the shield-makers street. In 1976 archaeologists began to uncover part of the Viking city of Jorvik in Coppergate. It was the beginning of one of the most important excavations to have been carried out in Britain. Wet soil conditions had preserved many things made of wood, leather and even cloth that would normally have rotted away.

Excavation work on the Coppergate site (left) revealed four rows of Viking buildings and hundreds of fascinating objects left by the people of Jorvik. Two of the rows have been reconstructed at the site. Thatched houses, workshops and shops are crammed close together along a narrow alleyway. Near the water wells, outside the buildings, are holes in the ground which served as Viking lavatories

Norman ships sail towards the English shores. Each ship has a Viking-style dragon's head at the prow, and a side rudder at the stern. The Bayeux Tapestry, from which this scene is taken, tells the story of the Norman invasion of England and what happened in 1066 at the Battle of Hastings.
As the Viking Age came to an end the Normans, themselves descended from Vikings, became masters of England

The Viking Age closes

In 1066 an invading Viking army, led by Harald the Hard-Ruler, sailed up the River Humber. Harald marched his men behind his banner, *Land-waster*, to Stamford Bridge near York. There, on 25th September, after a long and bloody battle, the Viking army was finally beaten by the Anglo-Saxons.

But the Anglo-Saxon rejoicing was short lived for news soon arrived that William, Duke of Normandy, had landed his army in the south of England. Shortly

afterwards, in October 1066, King Harold of England was killed at the Battle of Hastings and England had its first Norman king. The Viking Age was fading away. It had lasted for three hundred years.

In Scandinavia, the Christian kings of Sweden, Denmark and Norway had each begun to unite their countries under their rule. Viking settlers living in other countries had for a long time mixed and married with the people who lived there. The true Viking was no more – they had become French, English, Irish or Icelandic.

Today, traces of the Vikings can still be found, in the place names and in the language of the countries in which they settled.

We use a Viking word when we talk about *eggs, yuletide,* the *law* or *dying*.

If you live in a town whose name ends in *by* (farm or village), *thorpe* (a hamlet) or *thwaite* (a clearing) then you are living in what was once a Viking settlement. Wragby (Wraghi's farm), Scunthorpe (Skúma's hamlet) and Braithwaite (broad clearing) are all examples.

In the past few years archaeologists have made new important discoveries about the Vikings – about their ships from those found in the Roskilde Fjord, Denmark, and about their towns and way of life from excavations at Dublin, York and Bergen in Norway. The Vikings were law makers as well as pirates; merchants as well as looters. Their parliament was the first to be founded in Europe and their daring sea journeys led them all over the world, discovering new lands like America, Iceland and Greenland.

None of this would have been possible had the Vikings not been skilled craftsmen and boat builders *and* had they not been a fierce and proud people. Every year there are new discoveries to add to our picture of what kind of people the Vikings were and how they lived.

The people of Shetland remember their Viking origins in January every year when they celebrate the fire festival, **Up-Helly-Aa**

Viking timeline

Late 8th century	Vikings leave Scandinavian homelands. Danish and Norwegian Viking raids on Western Europe begin
793	Viking raid on Lindisfarne – first recorded Viking attack in Britain
860s	Swedish Vikings travel and trade in Russia and the Far East
around 860	Vikings discover Iceland
866	York captured by Vikings and becomes the Viking capital
885	Vikings besiege Paris
886	Danelaw: England divided into English and Danish kingdoms
911	Normandy granted to Viking chieftain, Rollo, who became the first Duke of Normandy
930	First Icelandic parliament held
954	Eirik Bloodaxe, last Viking king of York, killed. York ruled by English earls until after 1066
986	Eirik the Red settles in Greenland
985/6	Vikings sight America. Constant Indian attacks force them to leave
999	Iceland becomes a Christian country
1017-35	King Cnut (the Great) of Denmark on the English throne
1066 September	The Vikings, led by Harald the Hard-Ruler, beaten by the English at Stamford Bridge near York
1066 October	The Normans, led by William the Conqueror (a descendant of the Viking chief, Rollo), beat the English at the Battle of Hastings
	The Viking Age draws to a close

INDEX